GRADE BY GRADE
PIANO

GRADE **5**

SELECTED BY
IAIN FARRINGTON

Music from this publication is available in braille and Vista Score large print formats from Prima Vista Braille Music Services. **www.primavistamusic.com**

VISTA
SCORE

BOOSEY&HAWKES

Iain Farrington

Iain Farrington has an exceptionally busy and diverse career as a pianist, organist, composer and arranger. He studied at the Royal Academy of Music, London and at Cambridge University. He has made numerous recordings, and has broadcast on BBC Television, Classic FM and BBC Radio 3.

As a solo pianist, accompanist, chamber musician and organist, Iain has performed at all the major UK venues. Abroad he has given concerts in the USA, Japan, South Africa, Malaysia, China and all across Europe. He has worked with many of the country's leading musicians, including Bryn Terfel, Sir Paul McCartney and Lesley Garrett. Iain played the piano at the opening ceremony of the London 2012 Olympics with Rowan Atkinson, the London Symphony Orchestra and Sir Simon Rattle. He regularly performs with ensembles including the London Sinfonietta and the Britten Sinfonia, as well as all the major London orchestras.

As a composer, Iain has written orchestral, chamber, instrumental, vocal and choral works. He composed two orchestral works for the *Wallace and Gromit Prom* in 2012 including *Wing It*, a jazz guide to the orchestra. His organ suites *Fiesta* and *Animal Parade* have both been performed and recorded worldwide, and his choral work *The Burning Heavens* was nominated for a British Composer Award.

Iain is a prolific arranger in many styles, including traditional African songs, Berlin cabaret, folk, klezmer, jazz and pop. He is the Arranger in Residence for the Aurora Orchestra for whom he orchestrated all the songs in the *Horrible Histories Prom*. His organ arrangement of Elgar's *Pomp and Circumstance March No. 5* was performed at the Royal Wedding in 2011.

Published by Boosey & Hawkes Music Publishers Ltd
Aldwych House
71–91 Aldwych
London
WC2B 4HN

www.boosey.com

© Copyright 2015 by Boosey & Hawkes Music Publishers Ltd

ISMN 979-0-060-12769-4
ISBN 978-0-85162-940-7

Second impression 2018

Printed by Halstan:
Halstan UK, 2-10 Plantation Road, Amersham, Bucks, HP6 6HJ. United Kingdom
Halstan DE, Weißliliengasse 4, 55116 Mainz. Germany

Music origination by Jon Bunker, Iain Farrington and Sarah Lofthouse
Piano performance by Iain Farrington
Aural Awareness recording by Robin Bigwood
Cover design by RF Design (UK) Limited

CONTENTS

Note: All fingering has been added by composers or arrangers or taken from first published editions. Fingering has not been added to pieces where such markings do not feature in the original source material.

01 FULL PERFORMANCE & AURAL AWARENESS CD

The enclosed CD contains demonstration tracks for all pieces plus audio for Aural Awareness tests. Track numbers are shown in grey circles.

SIERRA

from 'The Rock Preludes Collection'

Play this impressionistic rock piece with a real lightness of touch. It should sound very easy and relaxed.

CHRISTOPHER NORTON
(b 1953)

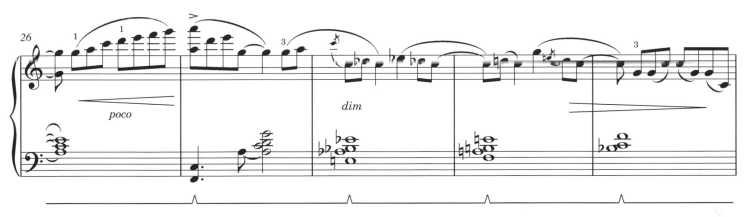

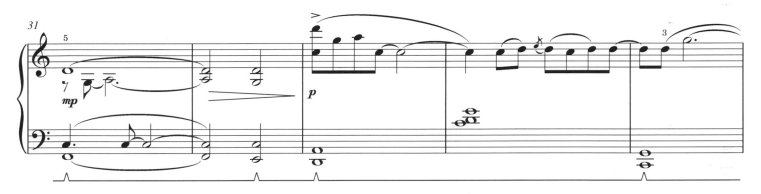

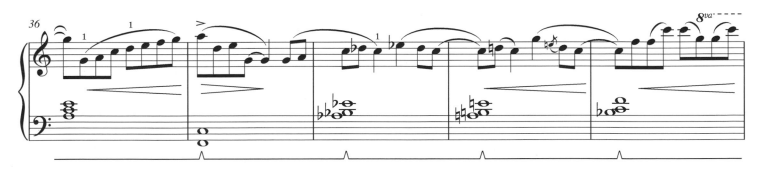

slowing to the end

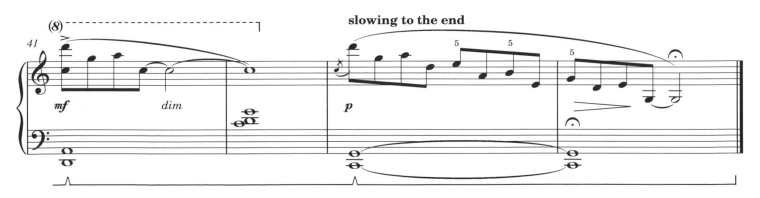

4

GAVOTTE
from 'Dances of the Dolls'

Amongst his vast output as a composer, Shostakovich composed educational pieces, including his 'Dances of the Dolls' in 1951. These are arrangements of earlier material, and this gavotte is taken from incidental music to the play 'The Human Comedy' from 1933–4. The gavotte is a stately dance dating back to the 16th century, and this piece has neo-classical elegance and charm.

DMITRI SHOSTAKOVICH
(1906–1975)

Tranquillo, semplice

© Copyright 1965 by Boosey & Hawkes Music Publishers Ltd for the UK, British Commonwealth (excluding Canada), Eire and South Africa

poco ritenuto **a tempo**

IN EVENING AIR

3

Aaron Copland was one of the leading composers of the 20th century, whose work seemed to define the sound of American music. The characteristic open harmonies, simple melodies and optimistic outlook of his popular works are reflected in this piano piece. It is a 1966 arrangement of a piece from his score to the 1945 documentary film 'The Cummington Story'. The work is prefaced by a quote from Theodore Roethke: "I see, in evening air, / How slowly dark comes down on what we do."

AARON COPLAND
(1900–1990)

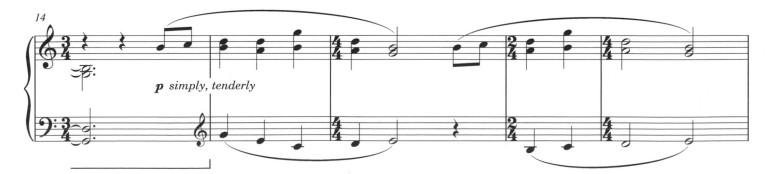

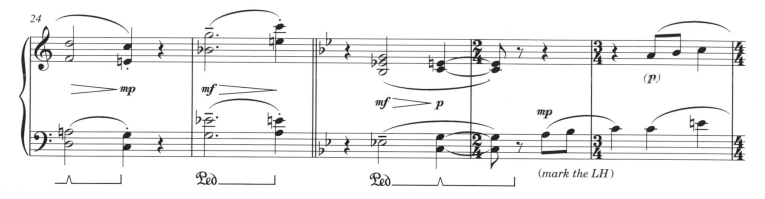

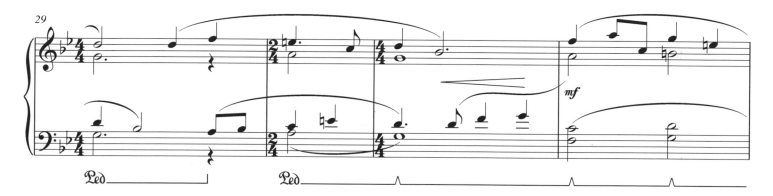

(weighty, singing tone)

8

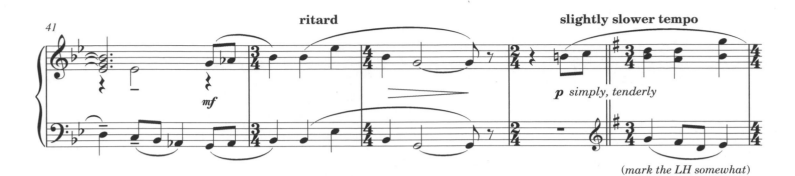

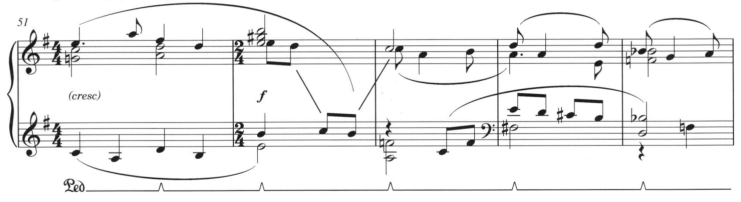

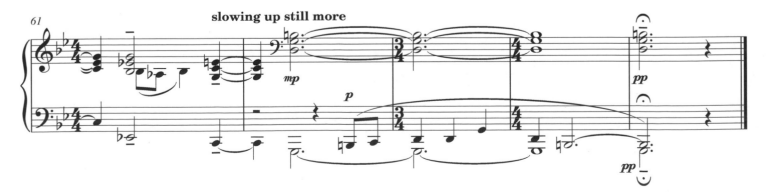

SCALE SPOT

Allegretto Con Moto by Frank Bridge (overleaf) is in the key of **F♯ minor**. Here is **F♯ melodic minor** scale: (Note the D and E are sharpened on the way up, and naturalised on the way down)

Here is **F♯ harmonic minor** scale:

Practise the exercise below with both hands together. It contains elements of both the harmonic and melodic versions of the F♯ minor scale.

AURAL AWARENESS 1

This activity will help you to better understand and enjoy the music that you hear and play. Like your fingers, your ears need a little practice, so try these activities with your teacher, listening to the CD, or to your teacher as they play the piano.

Listen to this short piece and try to respond as accurately as you can.
You will need to listen to it three or four times.

16

- Clap the rhythm of the opening four bars.
- Sing the first few bars of the tune.
- On which beats of the bar does the left hand play for most of the piece?
- Is the music in duple, triple or quadruple time? Is it in simple or compound time?
- Is the piece in a major or minor key?
- Describe the character of this music.
- Is the piece from the Baroque, Romantic or 20th century period?
  Give reasons for your answer.

ALLEGRETTO CON MOTO

from 'Miniature Pastorals (book 1)'

4

Frank Bridge was an English composer whose earlier works are in a Romantic style. He was Benjamin Britten's teacher and had a major influence on the younger composer. This piece is from a set of 'Miniature Pastorals' composed in 1917, and has a dainty wit that requires a light but precise touch.

FRANK BRIDGE
(1879–1941)

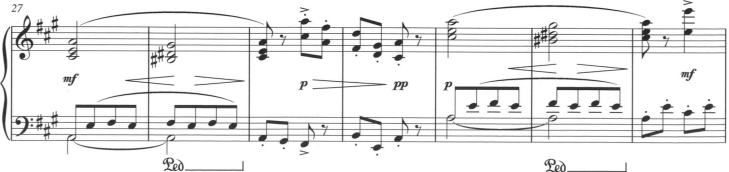

11

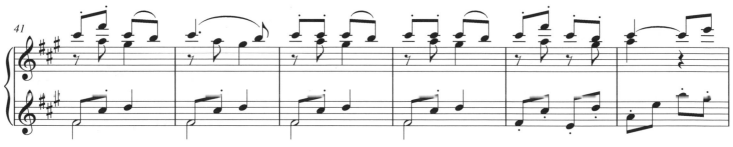

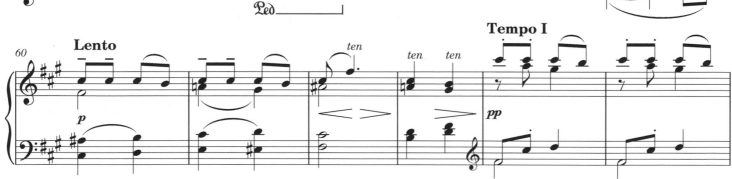

MARCH

from 'A Little Suite'

Trevor Duncan was an English composer who wrote much light music for radio, TV and film. He composed 'A Little Suite' in 1959, and the March was used as the theme tune to the BBC TV series 'Dr Finlay's Casebook' from 1962.

TREVOR DUNCAN
(1924–2005)
arr IAIN FARRINGTON

March tempo

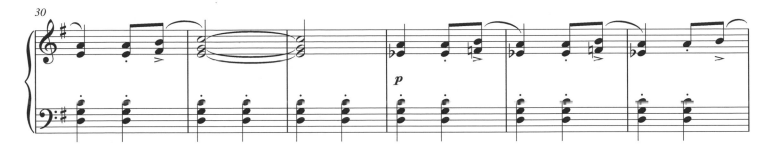

HAUNTED HOUSE

Arthur Benjamin was an Australian musician who worked for much of his life in England as a composer and teacher. This work was published in 1945 and is a brilliant depiction of a ghostly scene. The music trips along innocently before bumping with surprise into something unknown. Precise rhythm throughout is vital as well as clearly contrasting dynamics.

ARTHUR BENJAMIN
(1893–1960)

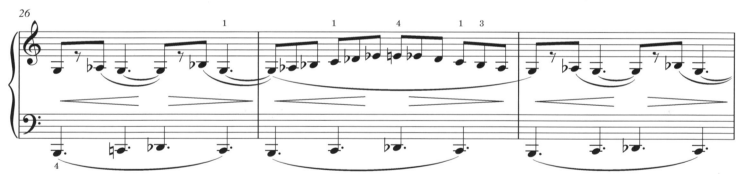

ECHOES

⑦

This piece is taken from 'Night Journey', a set of 24 miniatures of varying character composed in 2004. The echo effect in the right hand should be consistent throughout, using the pedal to sustain the lower chords.

IAIN FARRINGTON
(b 1977)

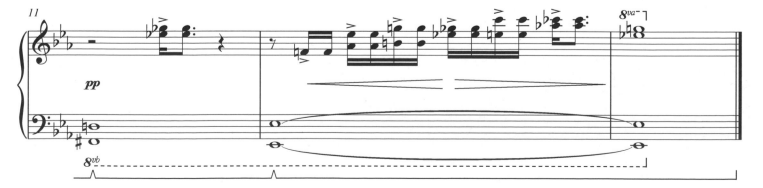

IMPROVISE!

In this exercise we'll use some of the features of Ellington's **Dallas Doings** (overleaf) to create an improvisation in a Blues style.

The left hand stave has a chordal accompaniment which sounds every beat. The right hand stave has a series of five notes to improvise with. (In bars 4 and 6 the previous bar's note palette should be used.)

Begin by creating a simple rhythmic pattern which can be repeated with different notes for the duration of the improvisation. (You might want to ask a friend or teacher to play the left hand part to begin with to allow you to focus on your right hand improvisation.)

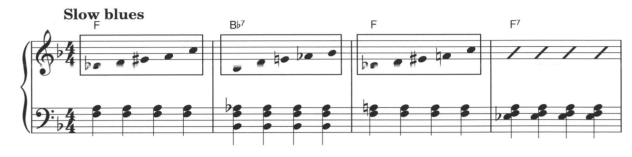

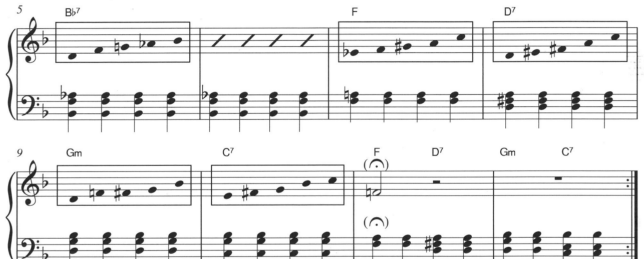

As you become more used to the feel and notes available, start to vary your rhythms, extend your phrases, vary your articulation and dynamics – and have fun! Remember that rests are important – you don't need to play on every beat. Here's an example of how your improvisation might start:

DALLAS DOINGS

8

Duke Ellington was a pianist, bandleader and composer whose work was pivotal in the development of jazz. 'Dallas Doings' was composed and recorded in 1933 by his band, and has an upbeat, lively swing feel. The dotted rhythms are 'swung' and should be fairly laidback, although the tempo is always strict and flowing.

DUKE ELLINGTON
(1899–1974)
arr IAIN FARRINGTON

THE LITTLE HORSE

from 'Pictures of Childhood'

Aram Khachaturian was an Armenian composer who gained great success with his orchestral music and ballets, especially 'Gayaneh' and 'Spartacus'. This piece is part of his 'Pictures of Childhood' composed in 1947 and requires much physical energy to maintain the galloping momentum!

ARAM KHACHATURIAN
(1903–1978)

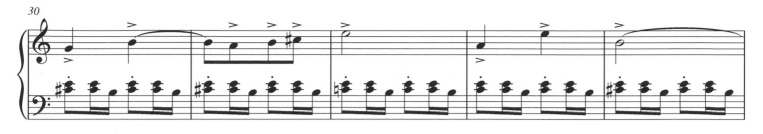

poco rit   a tempo

rit

LITTLE DOOR

Kats-Chernin is a composer based in Australia who has written much music for the stage, including the ballet 'Wild Swans' from 2002. The composer writes: "Apart from occasional deviation a semitone up or down, the piece is based on the harmony of [chord] G^7. There are no accidentals on the first page and it is possible to shift fingering positions in the beginning phrases. However, starting from bar 27 it is more about coordination of jumps in the left hand, built irregularly against the straightforward melodic movement in the right hand."

ELENA KATS-CHERNIN
(b 1957)

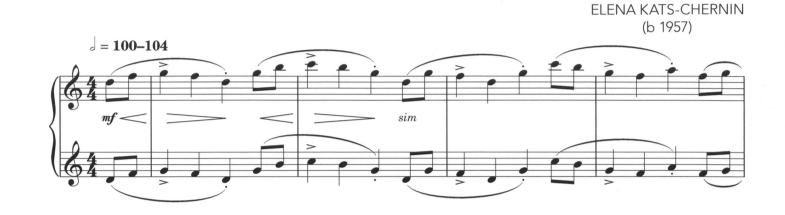

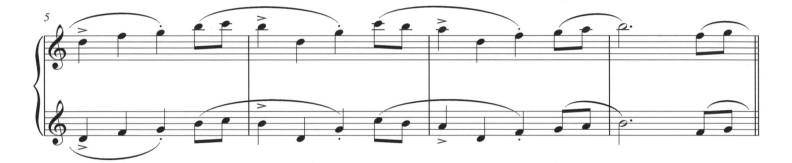

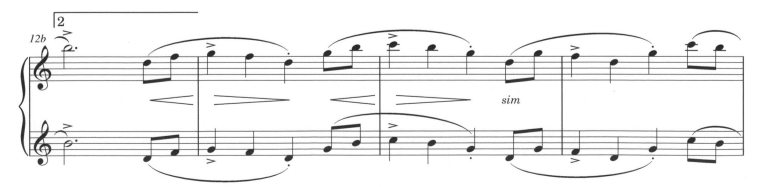

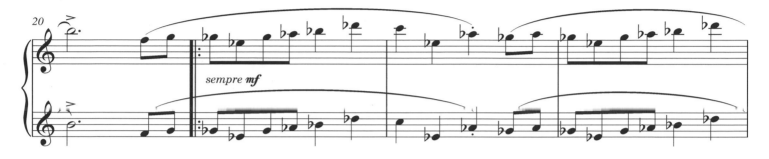

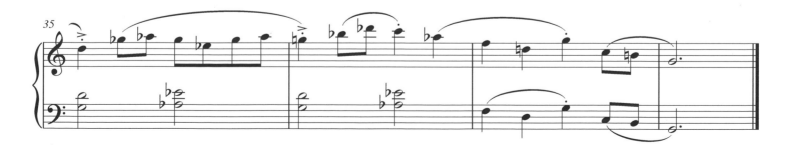

SIGHT-READING 1

Look for the clues about how this piece will sound:

1. What key is this piece in?
2. Clap the rhythm of bars 2 and 6 whilst tapping the pulse with your foot.
3. Look at the sequence of chords in bars 9–10. With the exception of the last left hand note in bar 10, in what direction and by what interval do the notes move?
4. Note all the dynamic markings and articulation.

Set yourself a steady pulse and off you go!

PAUL HUGHES

AURAL AWARENESS 2

This activity will help you to better understand and enjoy the music that you hear and play.
Like your fingers, your ears need a little practice, so try these activities with your teacher,
listening to the CD, or to your teacher as they play the piano.

Listen to this short piece and try to respond as accurately as you can.
You will need to listen to it three or four times.

17

- Sing the first few bars of the tune.
- Is the music in duple, triple or quadruple time? Is it in simple or compound time?
- Describe any changes in the tempo and dynamics of this piece.
- The melody is in the left hand at the beginning. Describe what happens to the melody in the middle of the piece.
- Describe the character of this music.
- Is the piece from the Baroque, Romantic or 20th century period?
  Give reasons for your answer.

SCALE SPOT

Cavalryman by Dmitri Kabalevsky (overleaf) is in the key of **B♭ minor**. Here is **B♭ melodic minor** scale:
(Note the G and A are naturalised on the way up, and flattened on the way down)

Here is **B♭ harmonic minor** scale:

Practise the exercise below with both hands together.

CAVALRYMAN

from 'Thirty Children's Pieces'

11

Kabalevsky was an important figure in music education in 20th century Russia, and composed a large amount of children's music. This is from his 'Thirty Children's Pieces' from 1937–8. Precise rhythm is crucial to convey the dramatic nature of the character, especially in the dotted rhythms.

DMITRI KABALEVSKY
(1904–1987)

POP LOOKS BACH

12

Sam Fonteyn composed a large amount of character pieces for orchestra that were used in TV and radio programmes. This piece was first recorded in 1970 and evokes the melodic patterns of Baroque music in a pop style. It has been used as the theme tune for the long-running BBC TV programme 'Ski Sunday' since 1978.

SAM FONTEYN
(1925–1991)
arr IAIN FARRINGTON

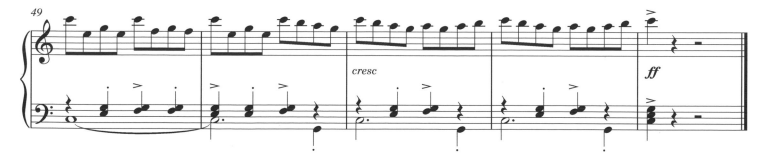

MUSIC THEORY

The extract below is from the full score of **Allegretto Con Moto** by Frank Bridge.

Study the score carefully before writing down your answers to the questions opposite.
The correct answers can be found on page 41.

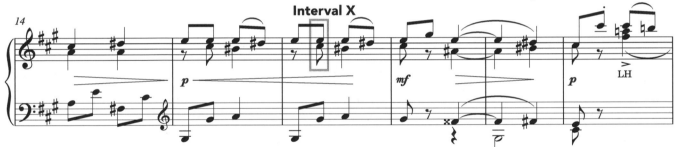

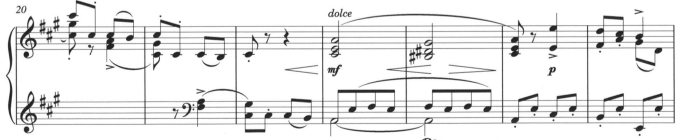

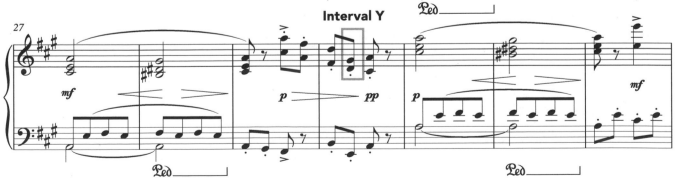

1.   What is the meaning of:

   a)   **Allegretto con moto**   _____

   b)   *dolce*   _____

   c)   𝄪   _____

   d)   *p leggiero*   _____

2.   Rewrite the first note in the left hand at bar 1 in the treble clef.

3.   Rewrite the highest notes from the upper stave of bars 27–30 for clarinet in B♭, transposing up a major 2nd. The starting note will be a B. Include a clef, time signature, key signature, dynamics and articulation.

4.   Describe fully the intervals marked **X** and **Y**.
     There should be two parts to your answer: the description (major, perfect, minor, diminished or augmented) plus the number of the interval.

   Interval X =   _____

   Interval Y =   _____

5.   Give the enharmonic equivalent name of the third note in the left hand at bar 10.

     _____

6.   Circle two of the five words below which describe the time signature:

   Simple   Compound   Duple   Triple   Quadruple

SIGHT-READING 2

Look for the clues about how this piece will sound:

1. What key is this piece in?
2. What do the following terms mean: **Andantino espressivo**, *con Ped*, **molto rit**, and **Lento**?
3. Describe what happens in the second half of bar 9.
4. What do the fingering markings tell you about what your left hand will play in bars 3, 5 and 11?

Set yourself a steady pulse and off you go!

PAUL HUGHES

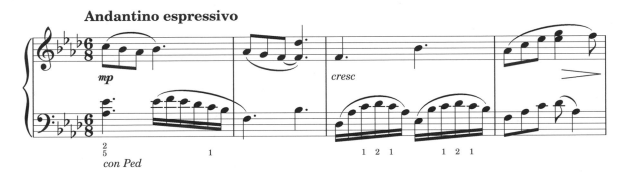

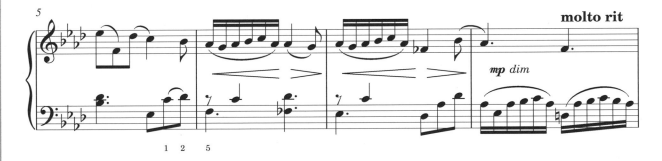

CLIMB EV'RY MOUNTAIN

from 'The Sound of Music'

13

'The Sound of Music' was written by composer Richard Rodgers and lyricist Oscar Hammerstein II in 1959. In the musical this song is sung by the Mother Abbess and is intended to give strength and courage. The climax of the piece should feel very grand and triumphant.

RICHARD RODGERS
(1902–1979)
arr EUGÉNIE ROCHEROLLE

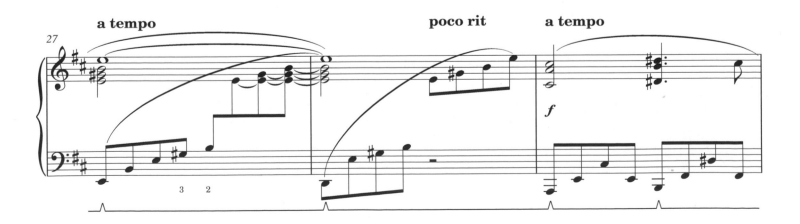

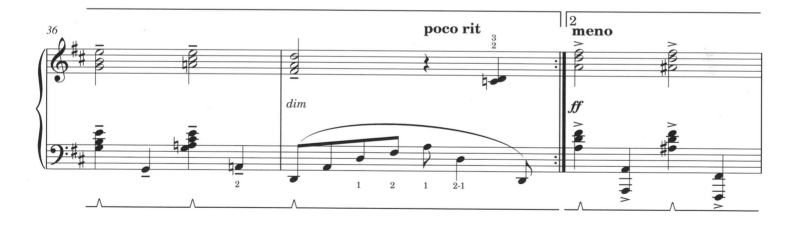

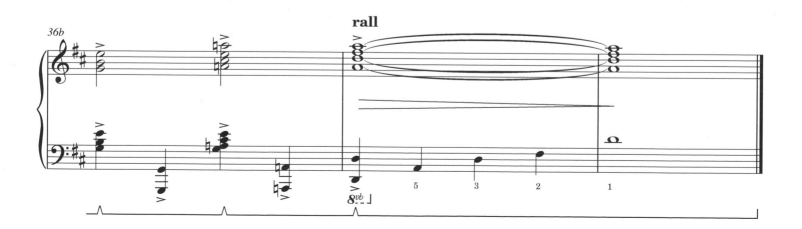

MONTAGUES AND CAPULETS

from 'Romeo and Juliet'

14

Prokofieff composed his ballet 'Romeo and Juliet' in 1935 and the work was an immediate success after the Kirov Ballet performed it in 1940. It contains some of the composer's most Romantic and melodic music, and this piece has become a particular favourite. Its official title is 'Dance of the Knights' and it depicts the two opposing families at a ball, with striding, aggressive music.

SERGE PROKOFIEFF
(1891–1953)
arr CHRISTOPHER NORTON

GRAN VALS

15

Tárrega was a Spanish guitarist who composed numerous works for the instrument, as well as transcribing other composers' pieces for his own performances. 'Gran Vals' was written in 1902 and is arranged here for solo piano. Its melody features a phrase that has become particularly well known as a ringtone.

FRANCISCO TÁRREGA
(1852–1909)
arr IAIN FARRINGTON

Moderato ♩ = c152

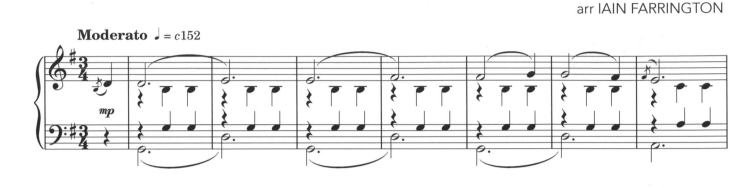

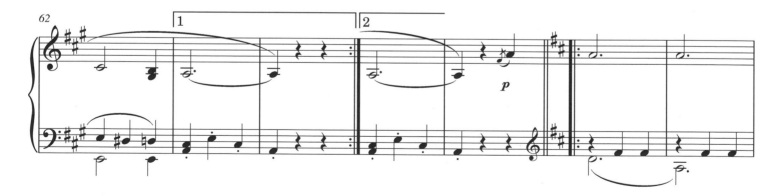

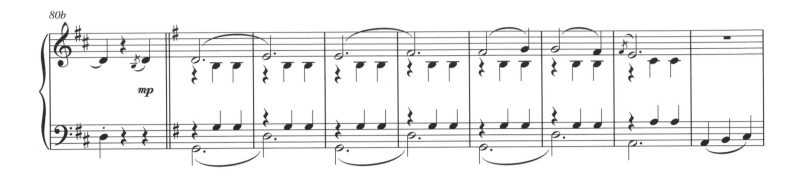

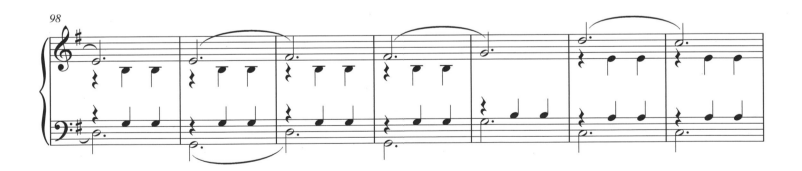

MUSIC THEORY (page 30) – Answers

1. What is the meaning of:

    a) **Allegretto con moto**   *Moderately fast with movement*

    b) *dolce*   *Sweetly*

    c) 𝄪   *Double sharp*

    d) ***p*** *leggiero*   *Quietly, lightly*

2. Rewrite the first note in the left hand at bar 1 in the treble clef.

3. Rewrite the highest notes from the upper stave of bars 27–30 for clarinet in B♭, transposing up a major 2nd. The starting note will be a B. Include a clef, time signature, key signature, dynamics and articulation.

4. Describe fully the intervals marked **X** and **Y**.
    There should be two parts to your answer: the description (major, perfect, minor, diminished or augmented) plus the number of the interval.

    Interval X = *Minor 3rd*

    Interval Y = *Augmented 4th*

5. Give the enharmonic equivalent name of the third note in the left hand at bar 10.

    D♭ (D flat)

6. Circle two of the five words below which describe the time signature:

    (Simple) Compound (Duple) Triple Quadruple

AURAL AWARENESS 1 (page 9)

16

Play this piece several times, and ask your student to respond to the questions that follow as musically and accurately as they can.

PETER TCHAIKOVSKY

Tempo di mazurka

extract from 'Tchaikovsky Album for the Young – 10. Mazurka'

- Clap the rhythm of the opening four bars.
- Sing the first few bars of the tune.
- On which beats of the bar does the left hand play for most of the piece? (1st and 3rd)
- Is the music in duple, triple or quadruple time? Is it in simple or compound time? (Simple, triple)
- Is the piece in a major or minor key? (Minor)
- Describe the character of this music. (A lively, dance-like composition)
- Is the piece from the Baroque, Romantic or 20th century period? (Romantic)
  Give reasons for your answer. (Rich harmonies)

AURAL AWARENESS 2 (page 25)

Play this piece several times, and ask your student to respond to the questions that follow as musically and accurately as they can.

BÉLA BARTÓK

extract from 'Bartók for Children (volume 1)', no 13.

- Sing the first few bars of the tune.
- Is the music in duple, triple or quadruple time? Is it in simple or compound time? (Quadruple, simple)
- Describe any changes in the tempo and dynamics of this piece. (There is a *ritenuto* and *diminuendo* at the end)
- The melody is in the left hand at the beginning.
  Describe what happens to the melody in the middle of the piece.
  (The tune moves to the right hand, an octave higher.)
- Describe the character of this music. (A sombre, pensive piece.)
- Is the piece from the Baroque, Romantic or 20th century period? (20th century)
  Give reasons for your answer. (Some use of dissonance)

NOTES

ALSO AVAILABLE FROM BOOSEY & HAWKES

Sierra (page 2) is taken from:

THE ROCK PRELUDES COLLECTION
Christopher Norton

ISMN 979-0-060-11638-4 (includes CD containing performance and backing tracks)

A stunning collection of 14 rock-inspired pieces from the creator of **Microjazz**. Punchy rhythms, rich harmonies and attractive melodies make these enjoyable works perfect for the concert platform as well as providing ideal teaching material.

Christopher Norton is an established composer, arranger, educationalist and producer, and has written stage musicals, ballet scores, popular songs and orchestral music as well as jingles and signature tunes for TV and radio.

Gavotte (page 4) is taken from:

DANCES OF THE DOLLS
Dmitri Shostakovich

ISMN 979-0-060-02407-8

Dmitri Shostakovich's *Dances of the Dolls* is a suite of seven pieces for piano – including *Lyrical Waltz, Gavotte, Romance, Polka, Waltz-Scherzo, Hurdy-Gurdy* and *Dance*.

Dmitri Shostakovich (1906–1975) was a leading 20th century Russian composer and pianist. In addition to his numerous concert works (including fifteen symphonies) he wrote a number of educational pieces.

Allegretto Con Moto (page 10) is taken from:

MINIATURE PASTORALS (book 1)
Frank Bridge
ISMN 979-0-060-01376-8

3 short character pieces for piano, written in 1917.

Book 2 also available (ISMN 979-0-051-24318-1)

Frank Bridge (1879–1941) was an English composer, conductor and teacher. His output included orchestral works, chamber music and short compositions for organ.

Haunted House (page 14) is taken from:

ANIMATIONS
edited by Hywel Davies

ISMN 979-0-060-11765-7

Animations is part of the Boosey & Hawkes **Piano Moods** series. In this volume the musical theme is movement.

Arthur Benjamin (1893–1960) was an Australian composer, conductor, and teacher. He is perhaps best known as the composer of the Jamaican Rumba. *In recognition for the publicity the work brought to their country, the Jamaican government assigned him a free barrel of rum every year! He also wrote orchestral works, operas and music for film.*

The Little Horse (page 20) is taken from:

PICTURES OF CHILDHOOD
Aram Khachaturian

ISMN 979-0-060-03482-4

A delightful collection of ten fun and whimsical piano pieces for young players.

Aram Khachaturian (1903–1978) was a Soviet Armenian composer, conductor and teacher. He is best known for for his Piano Concerto and the ballets Gayaneh and Spartacus. His music has reached a wide audience in the West through its reuse on film and television.

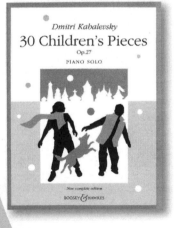

Little Door (page 22) is taken from:

Twelve One-Page Piano Pieces
Elena Kats-Chernin

ISMN 979-0-051-24630-4

Transcriptions and original piano works from the composer of the *Wild Swans Suite* and *Book of Rags*.

Elena Kats-Chernin is one of Australia's leading composers. Her diverse output includes operas, orchestral works, chamber and solo pieces, plus music for dance, film, and theatre.

Cavalryman (page 26) is taken from:

THIRTY CHILDREN'S PIECES, Op 27
Dmitri Kabalevsky

ISMN 979-0-060-11230-0

Thirty imaginative pieces for developing young pianists to learn and enjoy.

Dmitri Kabalevsky (1904–1987) was a prolific Russian composer whose work included four symphonies, five operas and eight concertos. He made a crucial impact on Soviet musical education and his songs and instrumental studies for children are now popular around the world.

BOOSEY & HAWKES

AN IMAGEM COMPANY